A Light Kindled

A Light Kindled

THE STORY OF
PRISCILLA MULLINS

By Tracy M. Leininger

A LIGHT KINDLED
Published by His Seasons
Copyright © 2000
All rights reserved

Layout and Design by Joshua Goforth and Noelle Wheeler
Illustrations by Kelly Pulley and Lisa Reed
Production Coordinator Cathy Craven

Scripture taken from the King James Version and the
New King James Version © 1982 Thomas Nelson Publishers

Printed in the United States of America by Jostens Commercial Publications
ISBN 1-929241-18-6

HIS SEASONS™

8122 Datapoint Dr.
Suite 900
San Antonio, TX 78229
210-490-2101
www.hisseasons.com

Dedicated to my father and mother, whose life goal has been to raise their children to know and love God. They have not only passed on the importance of walking in faith, but also the vision to impart the light of God's love to the coming generations.

And to the Pilgrims who sacrificed their lives to kindle the light of love and liberty on the shores of America—a land that shines with the brightness of God's glory.

CHAPTER ONE

New Horizons

The vast blue ocean stretched out as far as she could see, yet it was on the eastern horizon alone that Priscilla Mullins fixed her gaze. The *Mayflower* had set sail earlier that afternoon, and the shores of her beloved England had long since faded in the distance.

Standing alone, Priscilla swallowed hard as she realized that almost all she had known and held dear these eighteen years of her life was also fading into the past. A quiet ocean breeze caught wisps of her brown hair, causing them to softly dance around the delicate features of her face. She gently brushed them aside and continued to gaze east, where the shores of her homeland had melted into the watery horizon.

Would she ever again see her homeland? And what about her older brother, William? Priscilla took a deep breath and tried to hold back her tears, but her thoughts raced on. What of the future? What would become of them in this New World? They knew so little about it. When they had left the English port, familiar faces bade them "God speed," but that would not be the case at the end of this journey. Would there be even one friendly face to greet them? Once again tears welled up in Priscilla's soft brown eyes.

Just then, her father put his strong, caring arm around her shoulders.

"Come, my daughter, I have something to show you," Mr. Mullins said, leading her to the bow of the ship. "There," he pointed to the western sky. "What do you see?"

Priscilla caught her breath. "Oh, Father!" she whispered, "I have never seen such a glorious sunset. Such brilliant colors—such beauty!" For a moment they stood in awe, watching the ever-changing horizon. At length, Priscilla's wise father broke the silence.

"Priscilla," he said tenderly, "had you still been looking back toward England, you would have missed the beauty of this sunset. How often it is that we miss out on the blessings God Almighty has for us when we put our hand to the plow, but then look back. My dear daughter, as I look at the gold and silver in the sky, I can't help but think of the verse in Job which says,

> Yes, the Almighty will be your gold and your precious silver; for then you will have your delight in the Almighty, and lift up your face to God . . . it will be established for you; so light will shine on your ways.

"We are leaving much behind, but think on what we will gain. We are heading to a new home—and not just a home, but a land God will establish where we can worship Him freely and raise our families to follow Christ!"

Priscilla's heart stirred. A tiny seed had been planted. The timely words of her father, a man of dauntless faith and vision, filled her with wonder and expectation.

. . . Fear not, for I have redeemed you;

I have called you by your name;

you are Mine.

When you pass through the waters,

I will be with you . . .

Isaiah 43:1b-2a

CHAPTER TWO

Trouble Afloat

One month into the journey, the days seemed to pass in endless monotony for many on board the ship. Priscilla had learned at a young age that when she sought to serve only herself, the days passed by all too slowly. She therefore busied herself serving in any way that she could: sewing, cooking on calm days, and most of all, playing with the children. This also kept their minds off the unusually cramped quarters. The stormy season had come, and by the captain's orders, all passengers had to remain below deck.

"Priscilla, please tell us just one more story," six-year-old Remember Allerton coaxed. "Mother says we may hear one more before Mary and I must go to sleep."

Priscilla took a deep breath and tried to ignore the uneasy feeling in her stomach. The winds had been picking up all day, and it was quite evident that another storm was brewing. To keep the children from noticing the concerned looks on their parents' faces, she tried for hours to distract them with games and stories. Priscilla had even unpacked her childhood treasure—a little wooden Dutch doll. She allowed Mary to carefully cradle it as she told them of the times she had played with it in the shade of the walnut tree in her father's garden.

"Tell us again about your dolly," pleaded Damaris, who sat on Priscilla's lap. Priscilla tried to smile, in spite of feeling seasick, and silently asked the Lord for grace. The storm was increasing by the moment, making it difficult to hide her concern.

Without much warning, a tremendous swell caught the ship, shooting the vessel high into the air. The children clung to Priscilla for dear life as the ship plunged back down again. Suddenly there was a loud crack, and the ship's main beam splintered. The *Mayflower* shuddered, sending the lantern crashing to the floor. The flame sputtered out, and for a moment all was silent in the tossing darkness. Then, just as quickly, Priscilla heard sailors running about the hold and Captain Jones shouting orders to light a lantern and assess the damage. Her heart stood still, then it beat so loudly she could almost hear it over the raging storm.

"Dear Jesus," her heart cried out, "*do* protect us, and give me strength to act with courage." The terrified little Damaris, still cuddled in Priscilla's arms, sobbed uncontrollably. For the next few minutes, Priscilla's main focus amidst the confusion was to quiet her and comfort the other frightened children, all of whom seemed to have found a spot on Priscilla's lap.

With the girls somewhat calmed, Priscilla looked around, hoping to find out what damage had been done. Within earshot stood the ship's handsome cooper, John Alden, talking with the captain. His voice echoed the urgency of the situation, yet it was strengthened with the calm resolve that only a man of undaunting faith and courage could display at such a moment.

"Yes sir, Captain, I understand the imminent danger of sailing with our main beam cracked in such a manner. However, I have been made aware that one of our passengers has brought a large threaded shaft for his printing press. I feel sure, sir, that if we strengthen the weakest point of the beam with the shaft, with God Almighty's blessing, we may yet make it to the New World."

Just then, Elder Brewster called for all the families to assemble. "As the seas are fierce and our vessel in need of repair," he announced in a grave yet steady voice, "let us all call upon the Lord for His divine protection."

With the families now assembled, Priscilla put her arm around her younger brother, Joseph, as her father led the family in prayer. Priscilla could barely hear her father's words above the roar of the storm and the growing commotion in the hold, but deep within her heart she was again stirred with hopeful expectation. The seed that had been planted not long ago was beginning to take root.

Priscilla silently thanked the Lord for answering the prayer of her heart. Despite the raging sea around her, she felt a serene peace within. No matter where this journey led, no matter what happened along the way, they were following the Master; He would lead them to the New World.

"I can say with the prophet Isaiah," thought Priscilla, "Fear not: for I have redeemed thee, I have called thee by thy name; thou art Mine. When thou passest through the waters, I will be with thee . . .'"

CHAPTER THREE

His Strength Is Perfect

"Land Ho!" The long-awaited cry went forth on November 9, 1620. Priscilla leaned over the bow and anxiously watched as the shores began to form before her eyes. At first, only a distant gray line was visible on the horizon, but as time drew on, Priscilla could distinctly make out the forms of the tree-covered hills. Soon she saw the stark contrast between the cold, rocky shoreline and the piney forest beyond. She had never seen such thickly wooded areas. This new land seemed untouched by human existence.

Two days after anchoring, the weary, yet grateful, Pilgrims knelt on shore and gave thanks to God for their safe arrival. To some, no doubt, the land seemed harsh and the northern winds unwelcoming, but to Priscilla it held great promise. The bleakness of winter hid the treasures of spring, and the wind whispered the richness of the summer sun and the hope of an abundant autumn harvest. This was the New World, the land of which they had dreamed for years. True, at first glance, it did seem harsh. But what of God's hand? What of His providence? Priscilla bowed her head with the rest and silently thanked God for His faithfulness.

God, in His goodness, led the Pilgrims to an ideal location for their settlement. There, within a sheltered bay, lay over twenty acres of cleared land. They found not only fertile soil, but also four fresh springs of water. As the weather grew colder daily, and sickness threatened the lives of many already weakened passengers, the men promptly began construction on the first building—the common house. Living on the ship was not healthy for those who were ill. Therefore, as soon as the builders completed the common house, the weakest were moved to shore.

At first, Priscilla spent much of her time on land caring for the sick, but then, the long, cold, sleepless nights of nursing others wore on her until she, too, lay ill. Now all she had strength to do, in response to the kindness of others, was to whisper, "thank you." Priscilla's mother and the kind Mrs. Brewster remained almost constantly by her side, cooling her feverish forehead with wet rags and helping her sip warm broth whenever chills overcame her.

On the night of January 14, loud shouts and anxious cries roused Priscilla from her fitful sleep. She rubbed her eyes, blinked, then blinked again. Was she dreaming, or was it the effect of her high fever? Try as she might, she could only see a smoky haze. The air was thick, and she began to choke. The cries became louder, and her heart leaped in sudden terror when she finally made out the words: "Fire! The thatch has caught fire!" Her mind began to spin as sparks and embers fell from the roof. Then, through the glow, Priscilla caught a glimpse of the open gunpowder barrels and the muskets!

"Oh! Dear Lord!" she cried, as the gravity of the situation struck her. "Give me strength. I must get these out of here before they catch fire and explode." Her heart raced as she stumbled out of her cot toward the barrels. She painstakingly began to move one of the smaller barrels toward the door, when Captain Miles Standish, carrying his wife Rose in his arms, caught sight of Priscilla.

"Well done, Priscilla!" he yelled through the smoke. "I shall get help with the rest of the barrels. You make sure all the children are accounted for." Thus saying, he carried his feeble wife out the door and returned immediately, shouting orders to the others in his deep, commanding voice. Not long after the last barrel and muskets were removed, the roof over that very corner came crashing down in flames.

After the crisis passed, Priscilla fell exhausted into her father's arms and whispered, "The Lord's grace was sufficient, Father. His strength was made perfect in my weakness."

"God be praised for the foresight and the strength He gave you," Mr. Mullins reflected as he carried Priscilla back to the *Mayflower*. "No one has been harmed, and the main timbers of the roof are still strong."

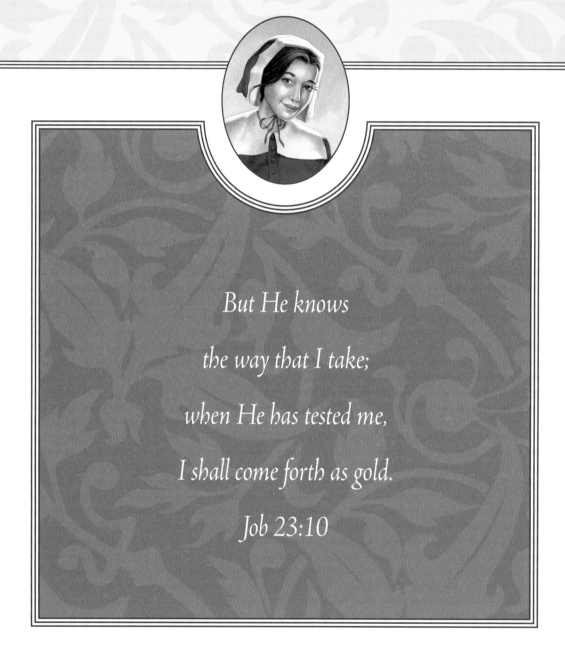

But He knows

the way that I take;

when He has tested me,

I shall come forth as gold.

Job 23:10

Father to the Fatherless

*P*riscilla, whose strong constitution had not failed through the long voyage, did not remain sick long. In a short time, she was again tending to the needs of others. The months that followed tested even the strongest hearts, marked as they were by endless sacrifice; yet God's provision sustained the Pilgrims.

God was refining Priscilla's faith as gold in a furnace. In late February, her beloved father died. Shortly thereafter, her brother Joseph died. The reality of the loss barely had time to sink in when Priscilla's dear mother became deathly ill. The shock of losing both husband and son had proven too much for her weakened body to handle. Priscilla tried her best to nurse her mother back to health, but nothing could be done.

Shortly after Mrs. Mullins' death, Priscilla knelt by her mother's empty cot and cried for some time, asking her Heavenly Father for strength to carry on. Now that her mother, whom she loved and admired so much, had died as well, Priscilla realized she was alone.

"Dear Lord," she prayed through her tears, "I have neither father nor mother. I know that You are a Father to the fatherless. But, Lord, who will be a mother to me? Who will guide me and teach me to be a wise woman, full of grace, tenderly loving those around me?"

After some time, a quiet peace came over her. She felt comforted with the knowledge that the Lord would provide in due season. The Brewsters graciously welcomed Priscilla into their home, and she was grateful to again be part of a family.

All but four of the women died that first winter at Plymouth Plantation. Priscilla had been so busy caring for the sick, mending clothes, cooking meals, doing laundry, and being a mother to the orphaned children that she hardly had time to think. Then

one evening, about a month after her mother's death, Priscilla knew she needed to be alone. Finding an old tree stump, she knelt and wept. Crying out to the Lord, she asked Him to fill the loneliness in her heart. Priscilla sat in silence for some time, her eyes turned heavenward. Not far away, she heard the faint sobs of a child. Little Remember Allerton ran toward her with tears streaming down her face.

"Priscilla," she cried, "Please, oh, please, hold me. When Father told me that Mother left to go to Heaven, I didn't know that—that she wasn't coming b-back. I miss her so very much! Who will—who will sing to me, and who will take c-care of me?"

As Priscilla wrapped her arms around the little girl, she planted kisses on her forehead. Remember stopped for a moment and looked deep into Priscilla's brown eyes.

"I love you, Priscilla. Will you be my new mother?" Priscilla answered her by hugging her tightly. A tear slid down Priscilla's cheek as she realized that she was not alone. There were still those who needed her, and comforting and caring for others was exactly the way her mother would have responded. The Lord had answered the cry of her heart.

The little community of Plymouth did its best to strengthen and encourage one another. Priscilla's admiration for John Alden grew daily. The tallest in the colony and the youngest leader, he was a gentle and kind man who always had a twinkle in his blue eyes and a song in his heart. On the days that the weather kept the men in, Priscilla often saw him leading children in a lively tune and doing his best to keep their spirits up. Sometimes he would stop and talk with Priscilla and offer her a word of encouragement. Priscilla began to look forward to these times more and more. In order to keep her heart guarded, she frequently reminded herself that he was a goodhearted man who would cheer anyone in need.

"Besides," Priscilla whispered to herself, "come spring, he will be sailing back to England on the *Mayflower*. I must remember to entrust the affections of my heart to the Lord's will alone."

Yes, the Almighty will be your gold and

your precious silver; for then you will have

your delight in the Almighty, and lift up

your face to God . . . it will be established

for you; so light will shine on your ways.

Job 22:25-26, 28

CHAPTER FIVE

Spring Blossoms

pring came at last, and hope seemed to grow with each new budding tree. The Pilgrims' strength grew daily as the beauty of the surrounding forests burst forth, rejoicing in the departure of winter.

Priscilla, who did not escape the eyes of the others, had blossomed into a slender and gracious young woman. Her dark eyes sparkled with the light of love and the law of kindness. It was not uncommon for Priscilla to slip away at every spare moment to enjoy the discoveries of spring and to talk to the Creator of land and sea, imploring Him for guidance and direction. The *Mayflower* would sail within the week, and Priscilla must decide if she would sail with it. Despite the difficulties, she was growing to love this new land. The trials of the winter had forged the community together with a bond that would not easily be severed. God had clearly led them here, and His hand had provided time and again. They surely would have all died had God not sent their Indian friend, Squanto. "Yes," thought Priscilla, as she stooped to pick a fresh blossom, "God has led me here and provided thus far. Will He not continue to lead?"

As it was, not one of the Pilgrims decided to sail with the *Mayflower*. Instead, they sent letters to loved ones back home and bade their last link to England farewell.

Priscilla stood hand-in-hand with Remember Allerton on the hill where Priscilla's parents and brother lay buried. From this point, they had a perfect view of the bay, and they both stood quietly in thought, watching the sails of the *Mayflower* fade into the eastern horizon. They had been silent for some time when Priscilla heard footsteps approaching. She turned to see John Alden. A deep blush covered her face as she realized that John, too, had decided to stay. John's presence, with his tall, strong frame and gentle, blue eyes, was always a source of comfort and strength to her. After watching

the *Mayflower* disappear between the sea and the horizon, John broke the silence.

"Look, Priscilla," he almost whispered. "God has seen fit to paint a glorious sunrise in the sky so that we may always remember this day."

Once again, Priscilla caught her breath as she took in the beauty before her.

"No king could pay to have the gold, silver, and crimson that God our Creator has displayed this morning. And no king could pay me enough to return to England," reflected John. "Priscilla, we in this colony are richer than any noblemen, for we have Christ and the freedom to worship Him."

"Yes," answered Priscilla. At that moment, the words her father had spoken aboard the *Mayflower* echoed in her mind.

> *Yes, the Almighty will be your gold and your precious silver; for then you will have your delight in the Almighty, and lift up your face to God . . . it will be established for you; so light will shine on your ways.*

As Priscilla finished quoting the verses from the book of Job, a sunbeam burst through the clouds and shone on the little town of Plymouth, lighting the whole settlement with its golden rays. The church on the hill, sparkling in the sunlight, looked as though its thatched roof was made of pure gold. Priscilla's thoughts went back to England and the Anglican churches with their fine spires and elegant carvings. How beautiful they were and how pleasing to the eye, yet to her, the humble little church in this free land was far more noble. The freedom to worship, and the love that filled the hearts of those within, made their church the loveliest place of all.

For the third time since leaving England, Priscilla felt the same stirring within her heart—only this time she knew that the seed had blossomed. How grateful she was that she had not boarded the *Mayflower* for its return journey. Her heart swelled with a surge of joy. To stay in this free land had been the right choice.

For lo, the winter is past,

the rain is over and gone.

The flowers appear on the earth;

the time of singing has come . . .

Song of Solomon 2:11-12a

CHAPTER SIX

"Why Do You Not Speak for Yourself, John?"

On May 12, 1621, the colony celebrated the wedding of Susanna White and Edward Winslow, both of whom had lost their spouses in the harsh winter. With the union came much rejoicing. Laughter rang out not only among the children, but also among the leaders of the colony. Winter had come and gone, its difficulties binding their hearts together. Spring showers had washed away the bleakness of winter, nourishing hope in the hearts of the Pilgrims. Now summer surrounded them with all its beauties. It seemed to sing a song of praise to its Creator, and the Pilgrims' hearts were warmed with the light of God's love.

When the *Mayflower* left England, Priscilla had been the only young woman of an eligible age for marriage. With over fifty single sailors and Pilgrims, Priscilla's heart and hand were highly sought after. Priscilla seemed either completely naïve to their attentions or to be purposely ignoring them. In truth, she was well aware of these things, but chose to focus more diligently on whatever task was at hand rather than let the attentions of others distract her. Although Priscilla was always gracious, she knew that in the end there would be only one man who could claim her heart and affections.

Priscilla admired twenty-two-year-old John Alden the most. Though he took time to encourage Priscilla, he never tried to impress her or gain her affection. Knowing that he showed just as much kindness to others in the colony was perhaps the reason Priscilla admired him so. Any man can be kind to the one he cares for, but few exhibit Christ's love so consistently that they can show equal love and concern to all those around them. In Priscilla's eyes, John was by far the most handsome with his light brown hair, defined facial features, and blue eyes that sparkled with kindness.

One day, after gathering reeds for thatch, John Alden and Captain Miles Standish walked back to the colony. Both were deep in thought, and both happened to be thinking of a slender, brown-eyed maiden of whom they hoped to catch a glimpse upon entering Plymouth. Unable to keep quiet any longer, Miles Standish broke the silence in a hasty and decided fashion.

"John, as my friend, I wish to confide in you an issue very near and dear to my heart. As you know, my beloved wife, Rose, died during those desperate months last winter." Captain Standish took a deep breath before continuing. "Well, I have recently noticed the fair and graceful Priscilla Mullins and have decided that if I could win her heart, I should be one of the most blessed men in Plymouth." Captain Standish explained all the reasons he felt Priscilla to be a perfect match, but John heard not a word. At the name of Priscilla Mullins his heart stopped, and as the Captain continued, it sunk deep into his stomach. He had intended, very soon, to make his own love for Priscilla known and hoped to win her heart. With a sick feeling inside, he inwardly argued with himself. "Have I waited too long? But no, I did not feel the timing was right. Captain Standish would be a very respectable man for her to marry, but it is I who have loved her all these months. Could I live in this colony, seeing her on the arm of another…?"

John's thoughts came to a halt as he realized Captain Standish was now asking him for a favor. "…therefore, John, knowing that you are as trustworthy and true a friend as a man can find, and that you are an educated man who could deliver this message with clarity and eloquence, I was wondering if you could be the messenger of my affection and call on Miss Mullins for me."

John cleared his throat and tried his best to hide his emotions. His mind reeled. It was proper to send a messenger on such a matter. "But, oh!" thought John, "Why did it have to be me?"

"Of—of course," John faltered. "I'm honored that you would ask me to deliver such a message; and may I be the first to—to congratulate you on your very f-fine choice."

The prayers and heart searching that went forth from John Alden that evening were both fervent and frequent. When he finally possessed sufficient grace to deliver the message, he did it with the confidence that God was in control. If God willed that Captain Standish win Priscilla's heart, then John was resigned that he would, in time, rejoice in it. He loved Priscilla deeply—so deeply that he desired the best for her, even if that meant marrying someone else. Such was the resolve of his heart as he knocked on the door of Mr. Brewster's home.

Now that Priscilla lived with Elder Brewster and his family, any suitors must first go to him before attempting to win her hand. Consequently, after John Alden had the blessing of that authority, Priscilla was called into the room to be consulted on the issue. Though Brewster felt Standish to be a good and respectable suitor, the ultimate decision would have to be made by Priscilla.

John rose as Priscilla entered the room, his heart racing as he tried to greet her in a calm fashion. Priscilla's cheeks flushed with evident delight when she saw him. John's heart sank. "Could it be possible that she has already heard the purpose of my visit?" he asked himself. "Is this the reason for her blushing?" John took a deep breath and courteously delivered his message. As a loyal friend of Captain Standish, John told of all the Captain's achievements, of his courageous deeds, and of all the reasons that Priscilla's union with him would be considered a comely match.

Priscilla, somewhat surprised that John would deliver such a message, patiently listened as he sang the praises of his friend. When he finished, however, she was not at all convinced that she should enter into a courtship with Captain Standish, for while John had been praising his friend's fine qualities, Priscilla had been thinking of twice as many that she admired in John. She sat and pondered these things for some time. Finally, unable to contain her thoughts any longer, she looked up at the messenger with a pleasant countenance and a smile playing on her lips.

"Pray tell, John, why do you not speak for yourself?"

Upon hearing these words, John's heart leaped for joy, and for a moment he forgot all about Captain Standish and the others in the room; indeed, he forgot everything but Priscilla. The look on his face revealed all he felt in his heart: the months of love he had stored up and hoped to show her, the agony of fearing he might lose her, and now the ecstasy of renewed hope that he might, indeed, have the heart of this fair maiden. The look crossed his face for a moment, and in the next, he blushingly regained his composure, bowed, and took his leave. It was not long, however, before he returned for Elder Brewster's blessing to declare to Priscilla and the entire colony the message of his own affections toward her.

As summer faded and the forest lit up in rich autumn colors, John Alden and Priscilla Mullins were married. All were jubilant in their union, but none were as delighted as the children they had so tenderly loved. When the ceremony concluded, Remember Allerton congratulated the couple by hugging Priscilla and bestowing a kiss upon her cheek.

Shortly thereafter, the Pilgrims and their Indian friends held an extended thanksgiving celebration, giving praise to God for the abundant harvest. John and Priscilla's hearts overflowed with gratitude.

Once again, Priscilla recalled her father's words as they left England just over a year before, "We are leaving much behind, but think on what we will gain. We are heading to a new home . . . a land that God has established where we can worship Him freely and raise our families to follow Christ!"

Deep in Priscilla's heart was the same stirring she had felt many times before. Tears came to her eyes. How she wished her father and mother could be with them. The Lord had indeed established this land where they could freely worship God and rejoice in His blessings.

Priscilla's face lit up at the thought that, should God see fit to bless John and her with children, they could train them up to follow Christ. Priscilla had a burning desire to impart to them a vision of faithfulness, that they, too, might be a generation that sought the Lord. She silently prayed, thanking God once again, and asking the Lord to enable her to someday pass on the seed of faith which her father had sown. He had given his life for this vision.

> *Except a grain of wheat fall into the ground and die, it abideth alone: but if it die, it bringeth forth much fruit. - John 12:24*

CHAPTER SEVEN

Passing on the Vision

Over the next five-and-a-half years, life at Plymouth continued to grow as more colonists joined the Pilgrims. They shared joys and trials as they learned the ways of survival in their New England colony. As they toiled and sowed in tears, they slowly but surely began to reap a harvest of abundant joy.

"Here's the milk, Mother," said four-year-old Elizabeth, beaming. "Father told me that I should bring it to you."

"Milk?" questioned Priscilla, who had stooped down to clean two-year-old John's face now that he had completed his breakfast. "Where did the milk come fr—"

"From Raghorn!" interrupted her husband, whose face glowed with excitement.

His eyes sparkled playfully as he continued, "Come, my dear Priscilla, and acquaint yourself with the fair and illustrious new member of the John Alden family. She has come all the way from England to join our colony and deserves due respect." John led the way out the door, and Priscilla followed, scooping up her little son John on the way. Elizabeth skipped along beside them, giggling and clapping her hands with delight.

"A milk cow?" gasped Priscilla as they rounded the corner and neared the pen. "Oh, John! Is she really ours?" Priscilla's pleasure showed in her voice, "Now I can make butter, we can have cream on our berries, and the children, John, will have milk to drink."

John put his arm around his wife and answered in a more serious tone, "Yes, she is ours, Priscilla. Four cows just came over on the good ship *Jacob*, and when the lots were cast, the Lord saw fit to give us this cow, Raghorn."

Seven years had passed since the first landing. Although the colony was thriving, life in this new land was still difficult. The Pilgrims endured many hardships, but the

Lord continued to go before them and prove Himself faithful. John and Priscilla's house, just off the only street in Plymouth, stood on a hillside. Every piece of furniture in their little home had been made by hand with the few tools and raw wood that were available. But with John's carpentry skills, Priscilla considered herself blessed with the best the colony could offer. Lavish comforts were low on the list of priorities, and only the bare necessities graced the homes of the Pilgrims during those early years. The long winter months kept Priscilla busy sewing all the clothes for her rapidly growing family. The summer months kept all of the Aldens in the fields as they tried their best to produce food from the rocky New England soil.

Did John and Priscilla consider their lives miserable? Not in the least! They thanked God for his faithful blessings through the hardships. They had a home, two children, and now that they had a milk cow, they felt like royalty.

"Mother," Elizabeth said as she dropped a small codfish into a freshly dug hole, "why do we put fish in the ground if we are planting corn? And why is it," she continued with a puzzled look, "that only the corn grows? If we plant the fish, why doesn't it grow, too?"

A smile danced around Priscilla's lips as she tried not to laugh at her daughter's honest question. "We don't plant the fish, dear," she explained. "We put it in the ground to nourish the soil. You see, the corn's roots like to eat the fish, and then the corn grows big and strong because it has lots of fish to eat." Priscilla glanced up as she stopped digging the next hole and looked into Elizabeth's blue eyes. "Our Indian friend, Squanto, taught us how to plant the corn this way. God sent Squanto to teach us how to live in this new land after that first long winter during which your grandparents died. If God had not sent Squanto, we probably would have all starved to death. But you see, Elizabeth," Priscilla said, putting her arms around her little daughter, "God led us here so that we could worship Him freely, and He would never abandon us. That summer, we planted lots of corn, and at harvest time there was such an abundance that we had a big thanksgiving celebration. Squanto brought ninety of his Indian friends, and the celebration lasted three whole days. The children ran and played, and the Indians challenged our men to some foot races and wrestling matches." Priscilla smiled, her gaze drifting far away as she reflected on the day. "Your father was one of the only men who could match the strong Indian braves. Shortly after our thanksgiving, the *Fortune* sailed into port, bringing thirty-five more colonists. They had not brought any supplies, and it was with heavy hearts that we realized there would not be enough food for us to survive the next winter."

"Mother," interrupted Elizabeth, her eyes wide, "were you or Father afraid that you might die before I was born?"

"No, dear. We were not afraid because we knew that the Almighty was in control of all things, and that He would continue to provide. We prayed that He might give us the strength that we needed. And do you know what?" Priscilla looked again into her daughter's eyes. "He *did* give us enduring strength! At one point, we had only five kernels of corn to eat each day." Priscilla placed five kernels in the palm of Elizabeth's hand. "And you know the end of the story, don't you?" Priscilla smiled, for Elizabeth knew the story by heart, though she never tired of hearing it.

"Yes, Mother," she answered. "God our Provider gave strength to all, and not one of the colonists starved to death that winter."

That night, as Priscilla tucked her two children into bed, she asked Elizabeth if she would pray for them. Elizabeth gently tucked the little Dutch doll that Priscilla had brought over on the *Mayflower* under her arm, and with childlike faith began her prayer.

"Dear God our Provider, thank you for the cow, the corn, and the fish to feed the corn. And thank you for Mother and Father and my little brother, John. Thank You that we live in this place where we can worship You. Dear Lord, please help me to teach my dolly to love You and to be a good little girl. Amen."

Priscilla's heart swelled with joy, for God her Provider had blessed her with much.

A tear came to her eye as she realized that her daughter, in her own childlike way, was asking God to give her the wisdom to pass on her faith and vision to the next "generation," which in this case was her dolly.

As the children drifted off to sleep, Priscilla whispered one of her favorite Psalms, "We will not hide them from their children, shewing to the generation to come the praises of the Lord, and His strength, and His wonderful works that He hath done."

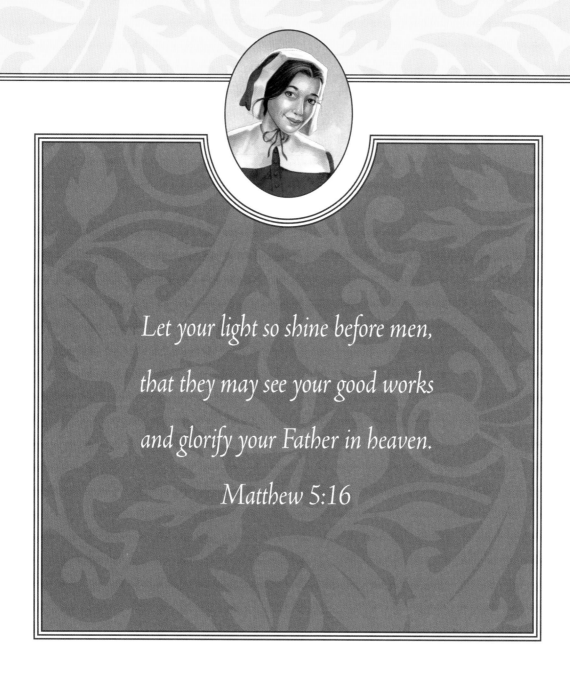

Let your light so shine before men,

that they may see your good works

and glorify your Father in heaven.

Matthew 5:16

Conclusion

From the beginning, John Alden was considered a leader in the colony. The youngest signer of the Mayflower Compact, John was also one of eight men called the "Undertakers," who selflessly labored for twenty years, at their own expense, to free the colony from the bondage of an unjust debt to the "Adventurers" back in England. John was known as one of "the most lovable of the Pilgrim Fathers." In 1632, moving his family to a large farm, he helped to establish the town of Duxbury. There he served as assistant governor for the greater part of fifty-three years.

John and Priscilla lived for the Lord, therein finding the secret in which the rose of true love can blossom and thrive. For where there are the weeds of pride and selfish ambition, the rose is crowded out and no longer receives nourishment from the sunlight of God's love. John and Priscilla's love lasted to the end. When the couple was last seen together in public at Josiah Winslow's funeral in 1680, they were still deeply in love—John, at the age of eighty-two, ardently adoring his wife, and Priscilla on his arm, admiring him with the same light sparkling in her eyes.

Captain Miles Standish and John Alden remained lifelong friends, not harboring any jealousy over Priscilla's hand. In fact, the harmony between the two families was such that John and Priscilla's second oldest daughter, Sara, actually married Alexander Standish, son of Miles Standish.

Of all the *Mayflower* passengers, it is widely believed that John and Priscilla have the most descendants. They were the parents of eleven children, each of whom embraced the faith. They were grandparents of sixty-nine children, and great-grandparents to nearly five hundred. To this day, there are estimated to be over a million Alden descendants. From their line came many illustrious leaders, including America's well-known author, Henry Wadsworth Longfellow, U.S. Presidents John Adams and John Quincy Adams, and former Vice-President Dan Quayle.

The Pilgrims were called to be set apart as a light in this new land. William Bradford profoundly wrote, "As one small candle may light a thousand, so the light kindled here has shown unto many, yea in some sort, to our whole nation."

Their light did indeed shine forth, not only to our nation, but to the uttermost parts of the world.

Author's Notes

Two things came to mind in writing this book. First, I desired to break the inaccurate stereotype that paints the Pilgrims as stiff, rigid, and cold-hearted. It is a myth that they strictly wore black and white and that they had personalities just as stark. The truth is, the Pilgrims held strong convictions, had a reverent fear of God, and were willing to sacrifice their lives to obtain His purposes. These kind and selfless people earnestly desired to walk in faith and love.

Secondly, I was reminded of the importance of living a life devoted to serving the Lord. The choices we make today will have a major impact on the generations to come. For example, had Priscilla decided to sail back to England to join her only surviving family members instead of establishing her life and faith in America, our country today would not have the same godly heritage. Just ponder, just for a moment, what America would be like today without the godly seed that was passed down through her faithful descendants.

My prayer for you, the reader, is that you would look beyond your present circumstances and realize that God, as the ultimate "Author and Finisher of your faith," has a divine plan for your life. The choices you make today will reap a harvest in the generations to come. May you always seek His face.